The COOLEST Cat Coloring Book

for humans of all ages

This book belongs to:

CatLady FITNESS

Business in the front.

It's finally here...

THE COOLEST CAT COLORING BOOK THAT YOU EVER DID COLOR.

If you are familiar with the Cat Lady Fitness kitty crew, you'll recognize the many quirks and themes over the next 50 illustrations – from Alfred's specialness, to my reign as King, to livin' it up on the beach, to foster Betty's newfound catnip banana obsession, to the antics of her three kittens, Ronin, Pickle & Blue...

But the **coolest** part of this, The COOLEST Cat Coloring Book? If you love cats or are a cat slave yourself, then you will definitely love and relate to all the kitty-crazed goodness on each of these pages **no matter what.**

And if you're asking yourself,

Can this book GET any cooler?

Hold your scratch pad, because this paperback comes with **a special surprise gift.**

I snuck THREE hidden symbols within these pages. They include a panda (because, if you didn't know, our human mom loves her some pandas), a squirrel (our favorite catio entertainment), and of course, a lizard (because... well, R.I.P. to all you little lizards out there).

Once you find all three of these hidden keys, visit **CatLadyFitness.com/coloringbook** and enter your info to **get an exclusive bonus coloring page** that is not available anywhere else! Download it, print it, color it, gift it, or frame it and hang it up with purrrride.

Oh! And remember to share any pages you color with us by tagging Cat Lady Fitness on Facebook and our human @Jazamina on Instagram.

Let's be honest, I'll probably be busy napping or grooming my lion-esque physique... but my human **loves** seeing stuff from you guys. It makes her do this excited dolphin-like squeal that scares the whiskers off my brother Alfred every time... and that's **always,** always worth it.

Slow blinks, head butts, & HAPPY COLORING,

SIR PUPPY

& the rest of the Cat Lady Fitness fam

high five!

4

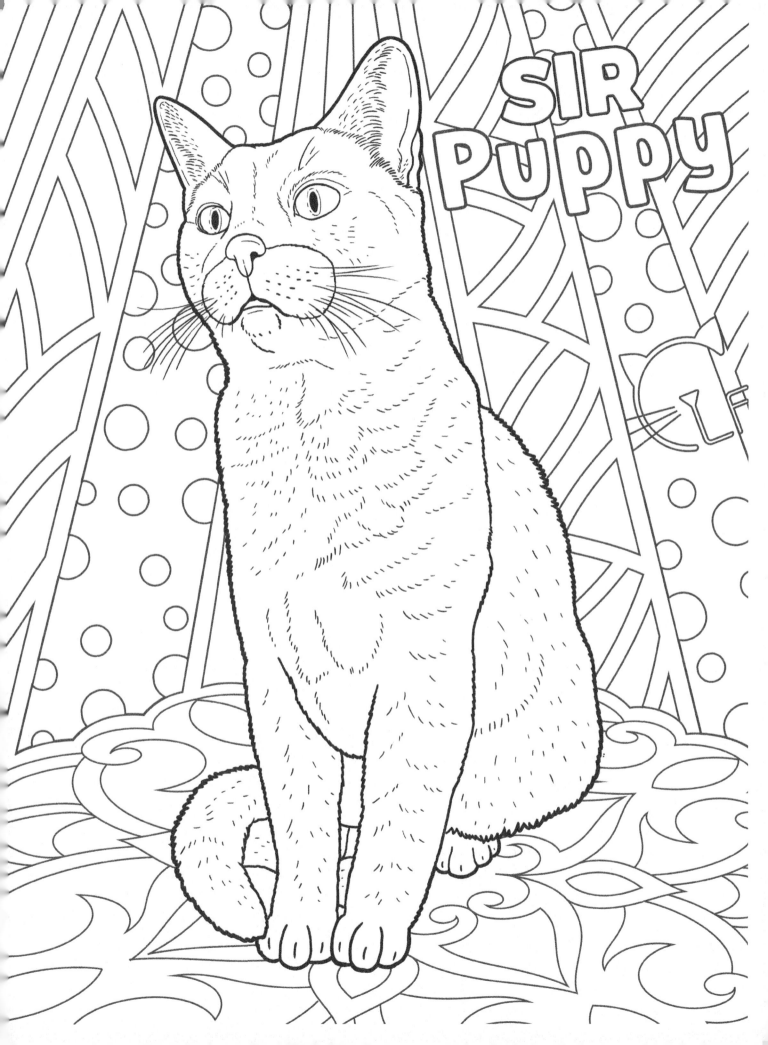

can I lick your
toes?

6

sshhh...

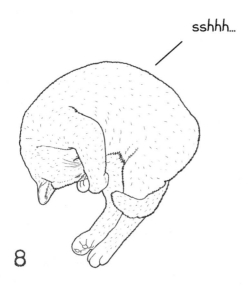

8

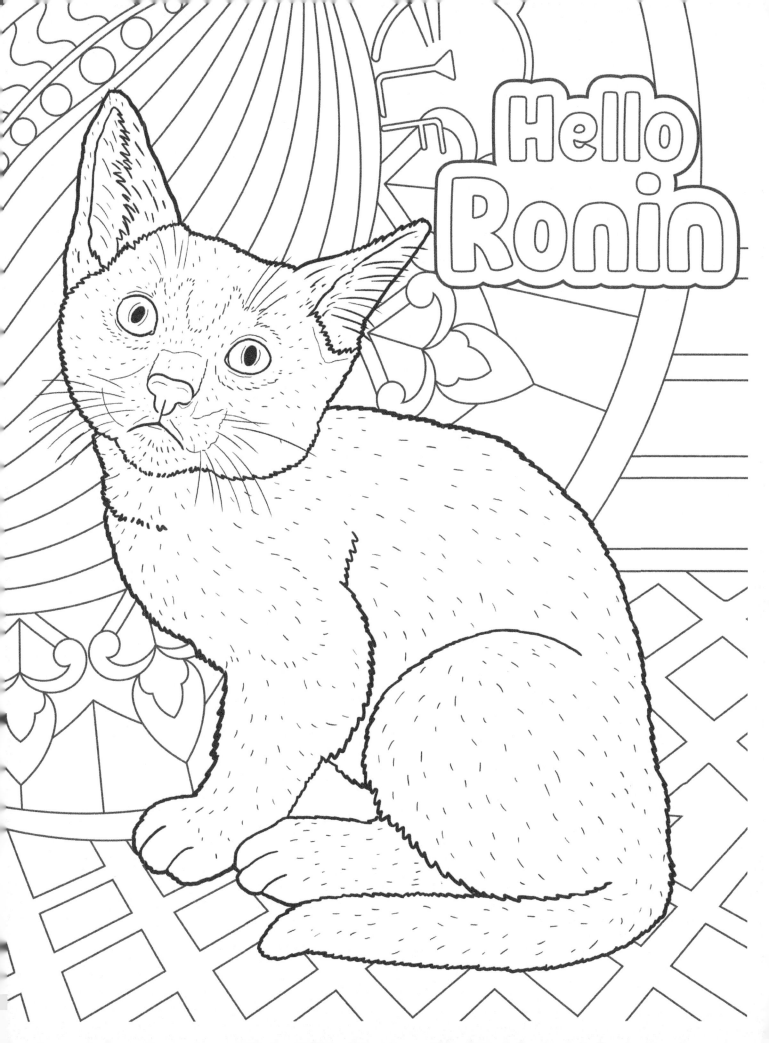

you're neat

so much skill...

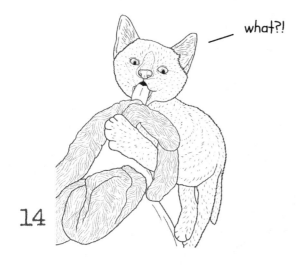

what?!

14

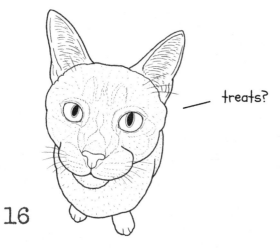

treats?

zzz...

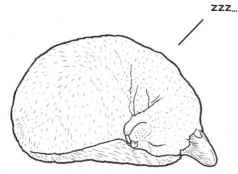

20

nice colors

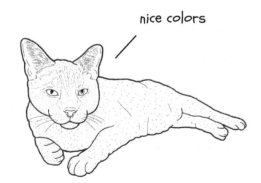

oh this?
It's vintage

wow you're good

26

oh to be young again

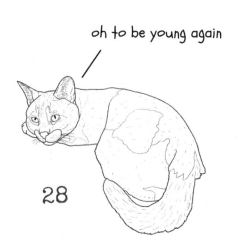

I IS CUTE

30

who ordered a toe
bean burrito?

mom who is that?

shh.. stay VERY still...

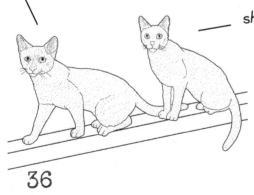

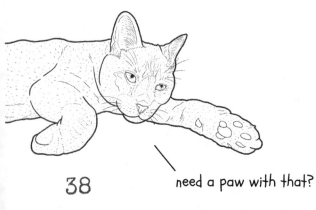

need a paw with that?

38

teach me your ways

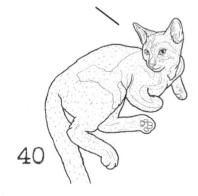

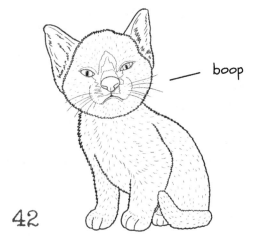

boop

42

find me yet?!

44

my word...

purrivate rooms
(do not disturb)

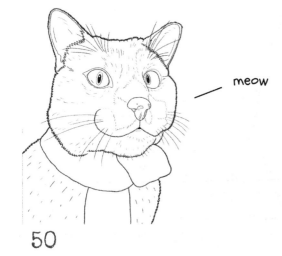

meow

Zoomies in 5... 4... 3... 2...

that crown tho...

I prefer rest days

54

help I stuck

woe is kitty

do u like my furdora?

stretch those
coloring fingers

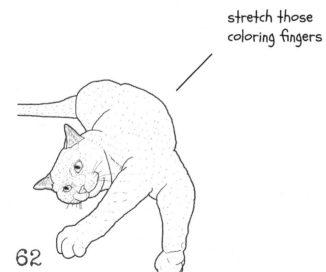

62

you're pretty

bleppity bloop

find me yet?!

ooo butterflies...

YAAAAS

72

at least one
of us works

what a mighty
tail you have

King of the House Lions

don't u eat my brother

dinner time?!

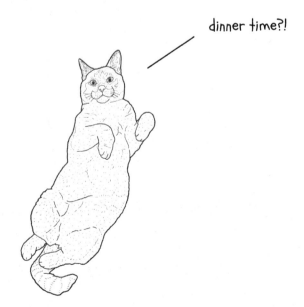

our mama is meowjestic

THE EMPURRESS

approves of your coloring skills

is there pawpurrnickel?

you're a natural

Sahara Dreamin

look, it's a meowmaid

If u were a cat,
I'd spend all
nine lives with u

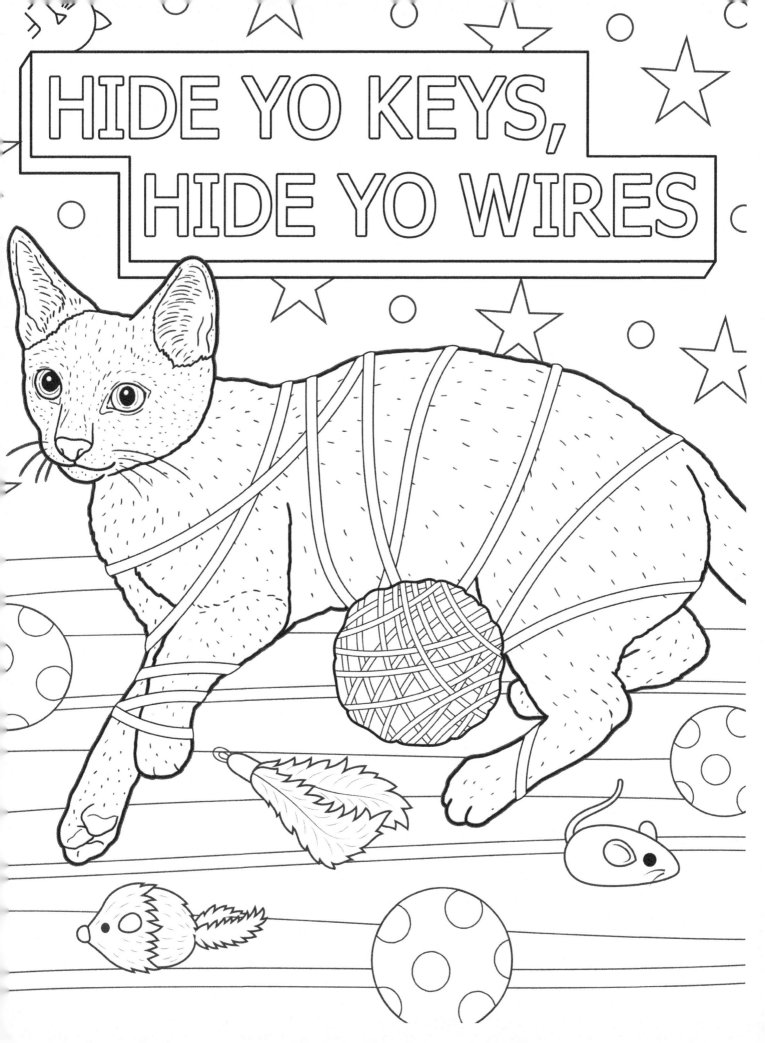

break it up, boys

94

jealous

totally

96

find me yet?!

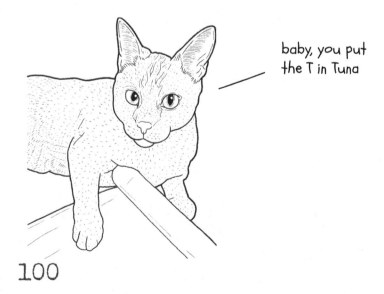

baby, you put
the T in Tuna

100

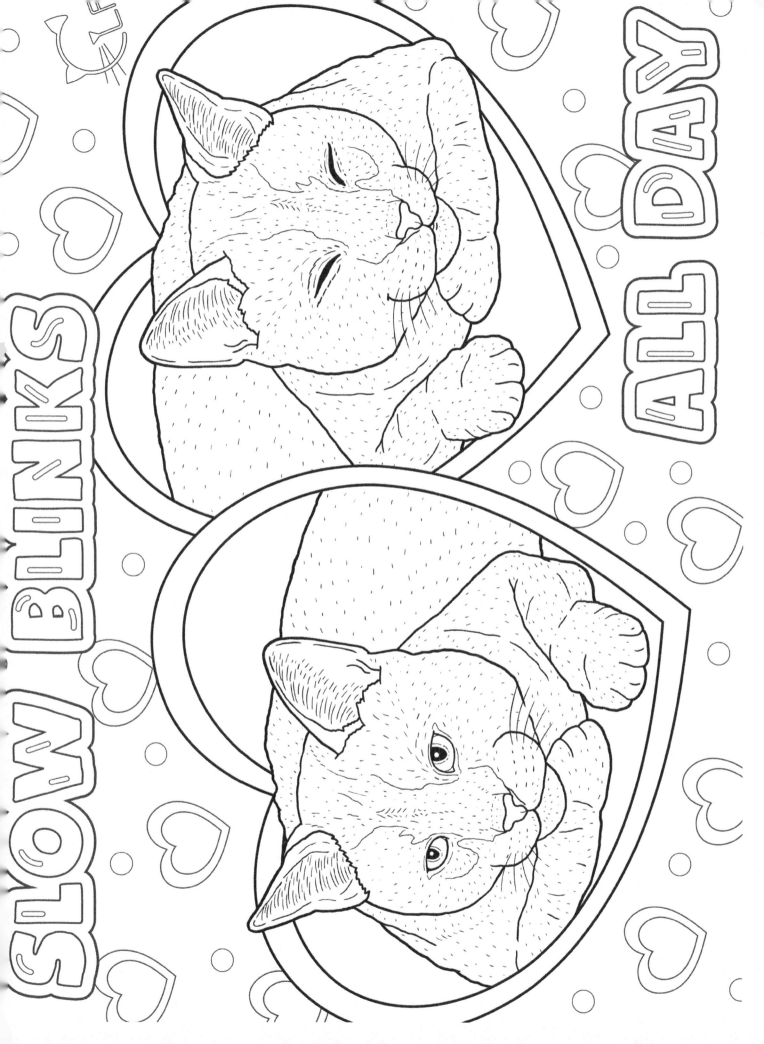

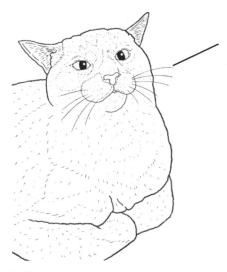

who is the cat's meow?
YOU are!

Let's be furriends

▶ Cat Lady Fitness

f Cat Lady Fitness

📷 @jazamina

🌐 CatLadyFitness.com

If u made it this far, know that u r special & loved & deserve the slowest blinks ever. Thanks 4 being u!

A giant thank mew to all of the ameowzing, suppurrtive, pawesome people who, 1) clearly put up with a ridiculous amount of cat puns, and, 2) have played a very important role in making this first coloring book a reality.

To all of our positively-minded and lovely YouTube subscribers and Facebook followers, thank you for supporting the content and growth of the Cat Lady Fitness channel past, present, and future. There is so much still to come and I appreciate each of you for being a part of it.

A special thank you to our first Purrtron on Patreon, Debbie Willoughby. Your support and thoughtfulness is so valued and I hope our exclusive community will grow even bigger soon!

To everyone who contributed towards Puppy's emergency surgery earlier this year and my unexpected foster care for Betty and her babies, I am so grateful for your generosity and love. Clair Douglas, Carmen Lecca, Lee Kaplan, Yong Rainey, Denise Bowens, Caijhmon Lowther, Debbie Willoughby, Ariel McGill, Alex Herchenreder, Ernest Beigl, Roberto Vazquez, Brittney Benson, Emily Forbes, Kristin Kamchan, Virginia Meador, Danielle Clothier, Elizabeth Tirado, Sam Alkaify, Diana Catcheway, Kevin Pietila, Maria Sanchez, Lorena Pardo, Grace Lee, Brian Lin, Alissa Garcia, Caroline Campbell, Ella Monte-Roby, Kelly Roggina, and anyone whom I may have missed... Your patronage and bigheartedness is forever appreciated. And, yes, the felines taking over my house strongly agree.

A very special thank you, especially from Pickle & Blue, to their forever dad Stew. They send me private text messages from their private little cell phones they keep hidden in their cat tree, just to express how happy and fortunate they feel to have found such a perfect home with you and Bear. Pickle promises to one day stop zoomie sprints across your face at 2am. Blue, however, never plans to stop sleeping across your neck. They are so grateful for you for taking them in. Thank you for being such a great human and friend and for always helping when I need it. BOOSH.

Thank you for all of the on-going help, from kitty nail trimming to flea baths to surrendering to Alfred's overwhelming naptime cuddle needs to litter grocery pickups to all other random feline and human needs that are way too overwhelming to list... to Tony. Your selflessness and patience is beyond measure. Almost inhuman. Which, actually, kind of explains the more cat-like napping habits...

Puppy & Alfred also want to send lots of love and gratitude to their Abuelita, who affectionately calls them her "grandkitties" and who never forgets their birthdays or to ask, "How are my grandkitties doing?" before hanging up the phone. Thank you for everything you do and for always supporting all of the many things I do with so much love.

Of course, none of this would have started without my soulmate O.G. feline fur child, Puppy, coming into my life. Who would've thought that this handsome boy – once flea-infested, living in a hot garage, and nearly surrendered to a shelter – could have helped shape my life and the lives of so many house lions around the world? Not me. Thank you to Puppy's Dad, who somehow knew that bringing him home to me would result in an incredibly fortunate cat and manifest into a priceless adventure full of love, creativity, and helping others. All the things that fulfill me to my core (in addition to having a real-life stuffed animal who purrs and cuddles on demand).

My heart is so full knowing we are all surrounded in so many wonderful, kind, caring people. I only hope you enjoy losing yourself within the pages of this fun-filled book as much as I enjoyed creating it. (Spoiler: There will be many more to come!) ♥

Panda hugs xx

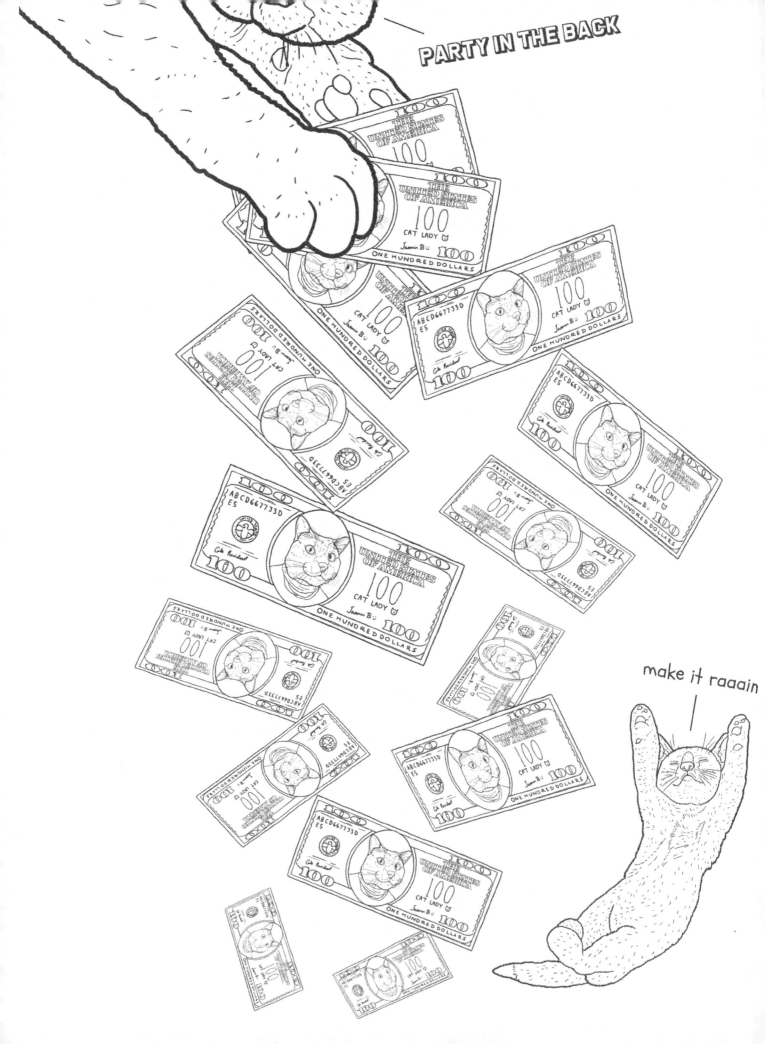

Made in the USA
Monee, IL
09 May 2022

96123749R00059